attara
PUBLISHING

Around the Year with JOEY

An Adventure Through the Jewish Calendar

בס"ד

AROUND THE YEAR WITH JOEY
An Adventure Through the Jewish Calendar

First Edition – April 2011
Copyright © 2011 by Attara Publishing

ISBN 978-1-935882-01-5

www.attarapublishing.com

Designed by SpotlightDesign

Printed by Sun Fung Offset Binding Co. Ltd., China

THIS BOOK WAS MADE POSSIBLE WITH SUPPORT OF THE REGALS FOUNDATION.

TABLE OF CONTENTS

 **Rosh Hashana – Jewish New Year**

JOEY

IN

OUTTA THIS WORLD!

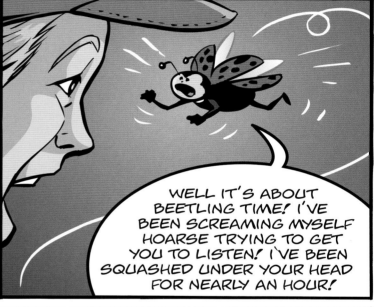

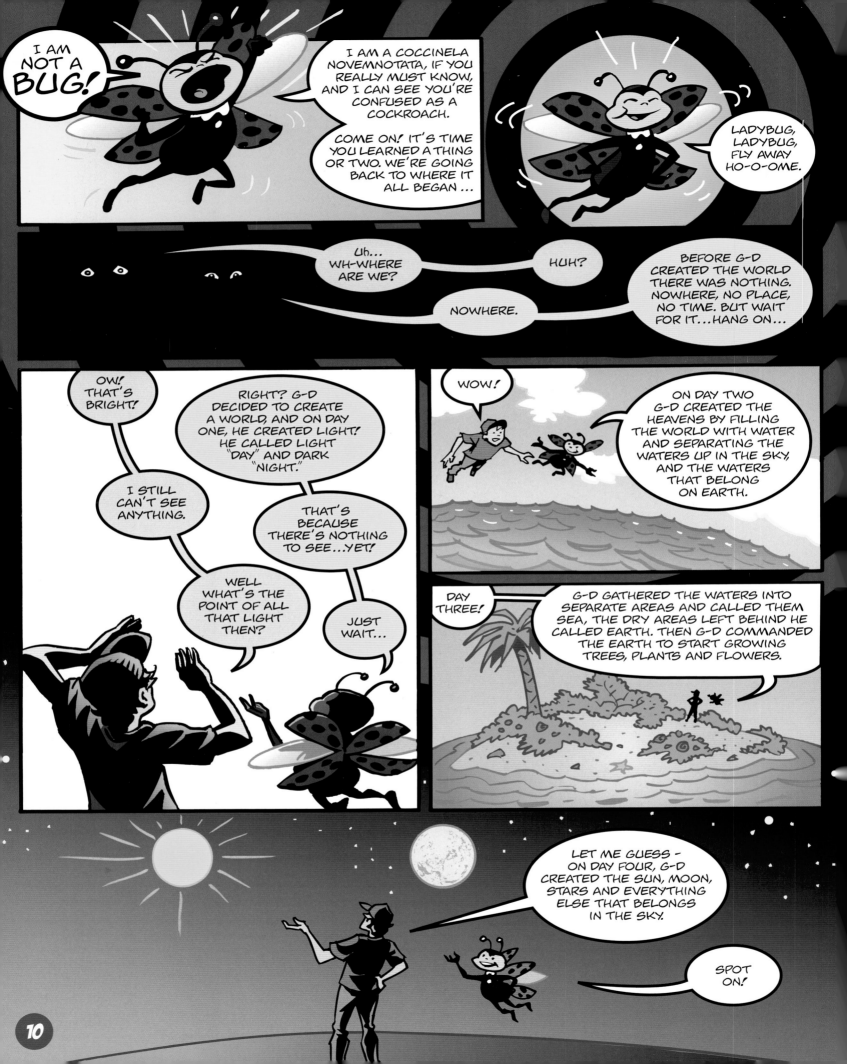

JOEY

AND HIS FRIENDS IN

TZEDAKAH MAKES THE WORLD GO ROUND!

...AND IT ALL COMES TO...38 DOLLARS AND 10 CENTS!

THAT'S BECAUSE JOEY GAVE AWAY THE MONEY HE WAS SAVING UP TO BUY A NEW CAMERA!

YOU ALL GAVE UP SOME OF YOUR OWN MONEY THAT YOU COULD HAVE USED TO BUY THINGS FOR YOURSELF. I GUESS THAT'S THE WHOLE POINT OF GIVING TZEDAKAH - CHARITY!

BUT WHAT DO WE DO NOW? WE NEED ANOTHER $26.90!

I'VE GOT AN IDEA!

PAY HERE

ROLL UP! ROLL UP!

SEE THE AMAZING, THE UNBELIEVABLE, THE INCREDIBLE...

MAN-EATING CHICKEN!

ARE YOU SMARTER THAN A SIXTH-GRADER? PITCH YOUR WITS AGAINST BENNY THE BRAIN!

HOW FAST CAN YOU ADD AND SUBTRACT?

A DIME A DOZE! CAN YOU WAKE HIM?

YOU'VE NEVER SEEN ANYTHING LIKE IT IN ALL YOUR LIFE!

MATCH MUSCLES WITH MOSHE! 25¢

GREAT WORK, EVERYONE. HOW MUCH DO WE HAVE NOW?

EXACTLY $51.75...OH, AND ONE BLUE BUTTON!

JOEY, CAN I HELP TOO? I HAVE A WHOLE QUARTER!

THANKS LEAH, EVERY LITTLE BIT MAKES A DIFFER-ENCE! IT'S NOT HOW MUCH YOU GIVE, IT'S THE FACT THAT YOU'RE GIVING THAT COUNTS!

THE END

Sukkot – Festival of Huts

JOEY

IN

WHO'S THAT KNOCKING?

The Adventures of JOEY in WHO'S THAT KNOCKING?

USHPIZ - WHAT? WHAT'S THAT?

USHPIZIN MEANS GUESTS IN ARAMAIC.

AND IT'S TRADITION THAT EVERY NIGHT OF SUKKOT SPECIAL GUESTS COME TO VISIT EVERY JEWISH PERSON'S SUKKAH AROUND THE WORLD...

HANG ON A SECOND. YOU'RE ABRAHAM AS IN ABRAHAM, ISSAC AND JACOB?

THAT'S RIGHT, YOUNG MAN!

MY SON ISSAC WILL COME TOMORROW NIGHT...

...AND HIS SON JACOB THE NIGHT AFTER THAT...

THEN WILL COME MOSES AND HIS BROTHER AARON...

...JOSEPH AND THEN KING DAVID ON THE LAST NIGHT OF SUKKOT.

WOW! I CAN'T BELIEVE THIS! WE JUST LEARNED ABOUT YOU IN SCHOOL!

REALLY? AND WHAT DID YOU LEARN ABOUT ME?

WELL...WE LEARNT THAT YOU HAD A BIG TENT, WITH FOUR DOORS ON EITHER SIDE, SO NO MATTER WHICH DIRECTION A VISITOR MIGHT COME....

...HE WOULD ALWAYS BE WELCOMED INTO YOUR HOME.

THAT'S RIGHT, JOEY ...COME TAKE A LOOK.

INVITING GUESTS IS A VERY IMPORTANT MITZVAH. IT SHOWS WE LOVE AND CARE FOR OUR FELLOW MAN, AND ARE READY TO DO WHAT WE CAN TO HELP HIM OUT.

...IN THAT CASE...!

HERE - PLEASE, MAKE YOURSELF AT HOME.

COME, JOEY... SIT.

Chanukah – Festival of Lights

JOEY
in

HERO OF THE HOUR

WE'RE SO **PROUD** OF YOU! THIS IS A HUGE OPPORTUNITY.

Uh, oh... LOOK AT THE **DATE**....

IT'S THE JEWISH NEW YEAR, JOEY! **EVERYONE** GOES TO SYNAGOGUE. WHAT ARE YOU GOING TO DO?

WHAT?! WHAT DO YOU MEAN? I'M GOING TO THE PROGRAM, OF COURSE! I DON'T EVEN KNOW THE FIRST THING ABOUT BEING **JEWISH**!

WE'LL SEE, JOEY...

THAT NIGHT...

IT'S **NOT FAIR!** THIS COULD BE MY CHANCE TO BE A HERO!

BRRR, IT'S **COLD** OUT HERE....

HELLO, YOUNG MAN.

WHAT'S BOTHERING YOU?

WH-WHO ARE YOU?

THAT'S NOT IMPORTANT... ARE YOU ALL RIGHT, JOEY?

HOW DO YOU KNOW MY NAME?

YOU SEEM TO HAVE A PROBLEM, YES? PERHAPS THIS WILL HELP?

THIS IS A **MENORAH**, ISN'T IT? I'VE SEEN ONE OF THESE BEFORE. LOOKS A LITTLE **DIRTY**, I'LL RUB IT --

WHA-?!

THE END

23

Purim – A Jolly Day

JOEY
AND HIS
FRIENDS IN

THE MAN IN THE MASK

OH BOY! THIS IS GONNA BE GREAT! NOW I'VE GOT TO START WORKING ON MY COSTUME...

You are invited to a PURIM MASQUERADE PARTY!

Date: Purim, 14th Adar
Time: 4 p.m. sharp to hear the Megillah
Followed by a grand Seudah-Feast!
Dress: Disguise yourself!
Charge: Dollar donation for charity.

PURIM MASQUERADE PARTY!

ATTENTION ALL STUDENTS! THE PURIM MASQUERADE PARTY'S ABOUT TO BEGIN. EVERYONE MUST MAKE THEIR WAY TO THE GYMNASIUM TO LISTEN TO THE MEGILLAH!

C'MON, KIDS, IT'S ABOUT TO START!

TORAH ACADEMY

REMEMBER, CHILDREN, WHEN WE HEAR HAMAN'S FULL NAME, WAVE YOUR GRAGGERS AND STAMP YOUR FEET!

VAYEHI BIMEI ACHASHVEROSH... AND IT WAS IN THE DAYS OF ACHASHVEROSH...

...HAMAN!

BOO!

STOMP!

THANKS, RABBI LEVI! AND NOW... LET THE MASQUERADE BEGIN!

JOEY

IN

THE AWESOME FOURSOME

JOEY
AND HIS
PALS IN

SOUL FOOD

GLOSSARY

CHAMETZ

Pesach is called the Festival of Matzot (unleavened bread). We must get rid of any other doughy substances, including cake, biscuits and other grainy food that has been allowed to rise.

ETROG

A citron fruit is another of the four plants. It symbolizes the human heart, as well as those people who are both learned and active in doing Mitzvot (good deeds).

GRAGGER

A gragger is the ultimate noise making instrument! When we listen to the Megillah (story of Esther) on Purim, we wave our graggers around and stamp our feet to silence Haman's name.

HAGGADAH

A Haggadah is our unique travel guide to the Passover Seder. If you've never heard of the Seder, it is the one night of the year, where we drink four cups of wine, eat Matzah, ask four questions, and participate in other strange and wonderful things!

KOSHER

Is a diet for Jewish people! It not only improves your body but your soul as well! Some requirements include not mixing meat and milk together, and eating only prescribed produce and animals.

MATZAH

Flat, unleavened bread, made of only flour and water. It is baked before the dough has had time to rise, and eaten on Pesach to remind us of the poor bread that we ate during our slavery in Egypt, and the miracles with which G-d set us free.

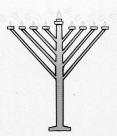

MENORAH

A beautiful golden candelabra that was lit in the Temple in Jerusalem every afternoon. To remember the Chanukah miracle, we light a Menorah each night of Chanukah. On the first night we light one candle, and add one more each night until on the eighth day of Chanukah we light all eight candles.

MITZVAH

G-d wants our earth to be a beautiful place to live, so He gave us Mitzvot, which are found in the Torah (Bible). These include acts of goodness and kindness, being respectful and helpful to others, and taking care of our wonderful world, as well as many more. How many Mitzvot have you done today?

CHARITY

PUSHKA

Get a positive boost each day by putting money into your charity box, otherwise known as a Pushka.

SHABBAT

G-d created the world in six days and rested on the 7th, also known as Shabbat. Starting on Friday evening with the lighting of Shabbat candles, on this day Jews all over the world go to synagogue and pray and spend quality time with family and friends. We also refrain from doing weekday activities.

SUKKAH

Sukkot is the best holiday; we get to go camping for a week! Well… kind of. We sit in huts (Sukkot) in our backyards to remember the time the Jews spent in the desert long ago.

TISHREI

In the Jewish calendar, which follows the moon's cycle, Tishrei is the 7th month and it's tons of fun! The festivals of Rosh Hashana, Yom Kippur and Sukkot all fall out in Tishrei, so get ready for shofar blowing, etrog shaking and synagogue, as well as lots of yummy home cooked meals!

't
liv
bea
fore
and J
word Mitz
These are inclu
them!

THE FOUR SONS

The Haggadah, the 'guide book' used at the seder, speaks of four sons; Chacham – the wise one, Rasha – the wicked one, Tam – the simple one, and Sheino Yodeia Lishol – the one who does not know how to ask. They all attend the Seder, and each one is taught the entire Pesach story in a way that they each can understand.

TZEDAKAH

Tzedakah means giving, and there are so many ways to do it! Every day put some change in your charity box for a positive boost. Other forms of charity include donating to your favorite cause, or helping a poor person with food and clothes.

USHPIZIN

As we sit in our huts on each night of Sukkot, another guest from vintage time visits us including Abraham, Isaac, Jacob, Moses, Aaron, Joseph and David of old. What a blast from the past!